A Nice Trip

by Kathryn O'Dell

Illustrated by Darryl Ligasan

OXFORD

UNIVERSITY PRESS

198 Madison Avenue
New York, NY 10016 USA

Great Clarendon Street, Oxford, OX2 6DP, United Kingdom

Oxford University Press is a department of the University of Oxford.
It furthers the University's objective of excellence in research, scholarship,
and education by publishing worldwide. Oxford is a registered trade
mark of Oxford University Press in the UK and in certain other countries

General Manager, American ELT: Laura Pearson
Executive Publishing Manager: Shelagh Speers
Senior Managing Editor: Anne Stribling
Senior Development Editor: Jennifer Wos
Development Editor: Diana Nott
Art, Design, and Production Director: Susan Sanguily
Design Manager: Lisa Donovan
Designer: Jessica Balaschak
Electronic Production Manager: Julie Armstrong
Production Artist: Elissa Santos
Image Manager: Trisha Masterson
Image Manager: Joe Kassner
Production Coordinator: Christopher Espejo

ISBN: 978-0-19-458915-4

Printed in China

This book is printed on paper from certified and well-managed sources

Phonics words

blows	giant	nice	they
Chad	glide	plants	this
city	grass	smiles	trees
Clare	huge	square	trip
fast	jumps	stones	wind
Friday	mist	stop	
friend	mother	then	

Sight words

a	her	no	she
an	I'm	not	tells
and	in	oh	the
are	into	old	to
can	is	on	up
fun	it's	sees	we
go	night		

New words

hello	ride	summer
look	Saturday	vacation

It's summer vacation.
Clare and her mother go on a trip.

Clare jumps in.
They go on a ride.

They go up fast.

The wind blows.
They go up into the mist.

Then Clare sees an old city. It's huge.
She smiles.

She sees plants and trees.
She sees giant stones. They are square.

They glide to the grass.

Clare tells her friend Chad.

Activities

A Write.

1. _____ are and her mo_____ er
   go on a _____ ip.

2. _____ ey go on a ride.

3. They go up fa_____ .

4. The wi_____ _____ ows.

5. They go up into the mi_____ .

6. They _____ ide to the _____ ass.

B Match.

1.

   •   • _____ are

2.

   •   • _____ ant

3.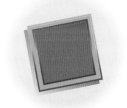

   •   • _____ ile

4.

   •   • _____ ity

5.

   •   • hu ___ e

C Check (✓) *Yes* or *No*.

	Yes	No
1. It's summer vacation.		
2. They ride on a plane on Sunday.		
3. The city is old.		
4. The stones are not big.		
5. The stones are square.		
6. Clare's friend is Chuck.		

D **What does Clare see? Check (✓).**

1. ☐ an old city   ☐ an old school

2. ☐ huge snakes   ☐ giant stones

3. ☐ plants   ☐ plates

4. ☐ trucks   ☐ trees

E **Write Clare, Mother, or Chad.**

1. _____ : This is not fun!

2. _____ : Can we stop?

3. _____ : Look!

4. Hello, _____ . I'm on a nice trip!

Notes

Before reading
- Children point to the cover and name things they know.
- Children try to read the title.

While reading
- Children listen to the story. Point to the pictures as they listen. This will help them understand the story. Example: Point to the plane interior, Clare, and her mother on page 4 for *Clare and her mother go on a trip.*
- Children listen to the story again and read along.
- Children read the story. Help them with words they do not know.

After reading
- Children point to the pictures and name things they know.
- Children read the phonics words, sight words, and new words on page 3.
- Children take on the role of one of the characters. Role-play the story.
- Cover up some words in the story. Read the story and stop at each covered-up word. Children say the missing word.
- Children do all the activities on pages 12–15. Check answers with the children.
- Children talk about the story. What did they like?